Enjoying the Library

Book E

WITHDRAWN FROM STOCK

Written by Jane Price

Published by Prim-Ed Publishing

Enjoying The Library

A Library Skills Programme For Primary Schools
Book E

The *Enjoying The Library* series comprises six sequential packages, catering for all Year levels in the primary school. The packages are self-explanatory and have been designed for use in any library, regardless of the number of resources available to the pupils.

It should be stressed that the activities in the series are designed to be used by both classroom teachers and library specialists.

The series involves a thorough library programme. The emphasis is on 'hands-on' experience as this not only caters for individual abilities and differences but also gives pupils the opportunity to explore the resources available in the library.

The aim of this programme is to make pupils independent library users who can choose and use appropriate, relevant library resources. Specific reference to many parts of the shelves has been made to enable pupils to become familiar with the wide range of subjects offered.

Each package contains some forty activities lasting approximately thirty minutes each. This provides a complete year-long library study programme. However, in many schools a second period per week is also given. It is important that in the second session all pupils are given the opportunity to borrow resources. Lower primary pupils enjoy this time to be read a range of stories or be given the opportunity to complete any library work.

Suggestions for further research are given in the packages for the middle and upper primary Year levels. Appropriately, a research question relating to specific classroom activities should be given.

Contents

Caring for Books

Library books are precious, as not only are they enjoyable resources, but they cost money, and other people will also want to read them.

Below are a few simple suggestions to make sure books are cared for.

1.   **Use a library bag.**

2.   **Keep your books out of the sun and damp places.**

3.   **No tearing, scribbling or spilling food onto your books.**

4.   **Always put your books in a safe place where you can find them.**

5.   **Always have clean hands before you begin to read.**

Revision

How do you borrow a book?

_____
_____
_____

Who works in the library?

_____
_____

To where do you return your books?

_____
_____

How many books can you borrow at one time?

_____

For how long can you borrow a book?

_____
_____

When is the library open?

_____
_____

LIBRARY
OPEN

List three examples of Reference material.

_____
_____
_____

Discuss this with your teacher.

Library Plan

Set up a plan of the library.

Cut out the sections of a library below and paste them on a piece of blank paper to make your own library plan.

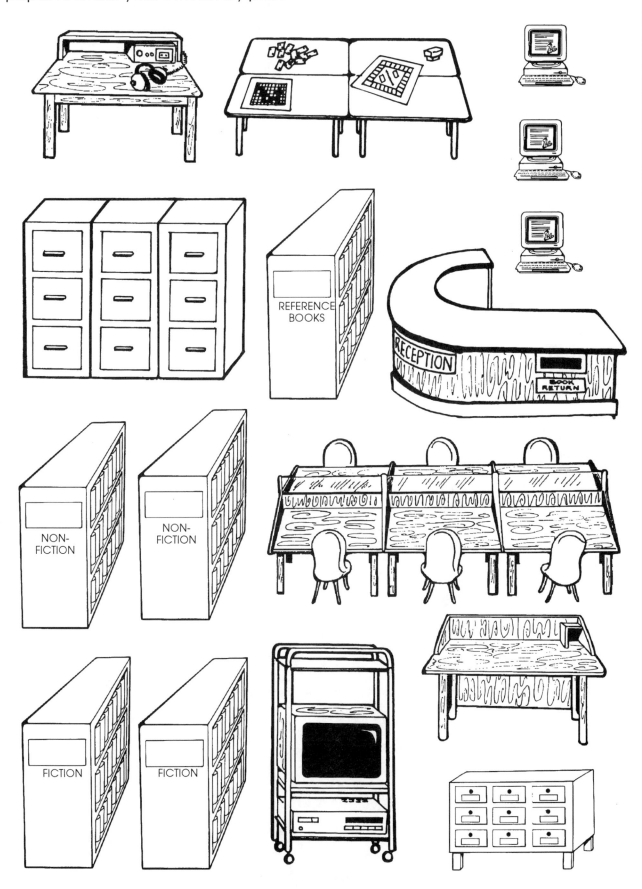

Fiction Section

1. What are fiction books? _____
   _____
   _____

2. How are they arranged on the shelves? _____
   _____
   _____

3. In the catalogue, either card or computer, we can identify a fiction book in several ways. These are:
   _____
   _____
   _____

4. Put the following authors in the order they would be found on the shelf.

   _____ Jean URE   _____ Norma KLEIN

   _____ Roald DAHL   _____ Olga MASTERS

   _____ Sue TOWNSEND   _____ Tim WINTON

   _____ Judy BLUME   _____ Joyce WINTER

   _____ Margaret MAHY   _____ Zacari BALL

F BAL	F BLU	——— DAH	——— ———
——— ———	——— ———	——— ———	
——— ———	——— ———	——— ———	

Parts of a Fiction Book

Title

Spine Label

Author

Choose a fiction book from the shelf. Open it to the cover page (usually found two pages in from the cover).

Who is the publisher of the book?_____

Find out what a publisher does. Write it down below._____

_____

Locating Fiction Books

What would you find on the spine labels of books written by these authors?

Zindel [ ]   Blyton [ ]   Martin [ ]

Martin [ ]   Briggs [ ]   Townsend [ ]

Banks [ ]   Voight [ ]   Thomas [ ]

Blume [ ]   Peyton [ ]

The catalogue or the computer can help you find the book you are looking for if you know the:

A _____

T _____

Write down the titles of two books you have read. Find them in the catalogue or on the computer.

1. _____

2. _____

Explain the process you went through to find these books.

_____

_____

_____

_____

Locate the books on the shelves.

Picture Books

What are picture books? _____

_____

_____

List some features of picture books.

_____

_____

Choose a picture book from the fiction shelf. Write down the:

Author : _____

Title: _____

Spine Label:

Publisher: _____

Illustrator : _____

Read the picture book.

Choose one of the characters in the book and write about him/her.

_____

_____

_____

_____

_____

_____

_____

_____

_____

Draw a picture of your character.

Short Stories

What are short stories?

_____

_____

_____

_____

Your teacher will read you a short story.

What are some of the features of a short story?

_____

_____

_____

_____

_____

_____

_____

_____

Did you enjoy the short story that was read to you? Why/Why not?

_____

_____

_____

_____

_____

_____

_____

_____

_____

_____

_____

_____

_____

_____

_____

Novels

1. What is a novel? _____
   _____
   _____

2. List six different themes for novels:

   (a) _____

   (b) _____

   (c) _____

   (d) _____

   (e) _____

   (f) _____

3. Which of the above themes do you like? _____
   Do you read mainly this kind or do you read a mixture?

   _____

4. Select a novel. Identify the following:

   (a)   Author: _____

   (b)   Title: _____

   (c)   Contents page: _____

   (d)   Publisher: _____

   (e)   Dedicated to: _____

   (f)   A summary: _____

   (g)   Other titles by the author: _____

   (h)   About the author: _____

Fiction Book Review

Locate a fiction book you would like to read.

When you have finished reading it, answer this sheet.

Author:_____

Title:_____

Illustrator:_____

Spine Label:_____

Publisher:_____

Nasty Characters:_____

_____

Nice Characters:_____

_____

What was the story about?

_____

_____

_____

_____

_____

_____

_____

_____

Did you like or dislike the story? Why/Why not?

_____

_____

_____

_____

_____

_____

_____

_____

_____

_____

_____

Fiction Quiz

1. What are fiction books? _____
   _____
   _____

2. Give three examples of the types of fiction books available.

   (a) _____

   (b) _____

   (c) _____

3. What are the main differences among the novels, short stories and picture books?

   _____
   _____
   _____
   _____
   _____

4. Which do you prefer to read? _____

   Why? _____
   _____
   _____
   _____

5. Are fiction books arranged on the shelf in any special way?

   _____
   _____
   _____
   _____

Fiction Sleuth

A	C	Z	T	R	E	V	I	E	W	E	B	E	L	T	I	T
S	H	O	R	T	S	T	O	R	Y	M	C	F	D	E	F	G
S	A	H	L	I	B	R	A	I	F	A	M	I	L	Y	J	K
E	R	L	I	B	R	A	R	Y	L	N	M	C	R	S	K	N
I	A	O	A	D	V	E	N	T	U	R	E	T	O	H	O	S
R	C	P	Q	R	S	P	T	U	V	U	W	I	M	E	O	P
O	T	X	R	Y	Z	U	A	N	B	S	C	O	A	L	B	I
T	E	B	O	O	K	B	D	O	E	S	F	N	N	V	E	N
S	R	S	H	H	I	L	J	V	K	R	L	M	C	E	R	E
T	S	E	T	O	P	I	Q	E	R	O	S	T	E	S	U	L
S	U	M	U	W	Y	S	Y	I	Z	H	A	B	C	D	T	A
O	E	E	A	L	P	H	A	B	E	T	I	C	A	L	C	D
H	G	H	I	J	K	E	L	M	N	U	O	P	Q	R	I	E
G	S	T	R	A	w	R	X	B	Z	A	A	F	C	R	P	L

Locate these words

Adventure
Alphabetical
Author
Author's Surname
Book
Characters
Family
Fiction
Ghost Stories
Library

Novel
Picture Book
Publisher
Review
Romance
Shelves
Short Story
Spine Label
Title
Themes

Non-fiction

What are non-fiction books?

_____

_____

Who was Dewey?_____

_____

How are non-fiction books arranged on the shelf?_____

_____

Number the following spine labels in the correct order:

219 FRA	623 PRI	796 SPO	001 COM	913 GEO
_____	_____	_____	_____	_____

Choose a non-fiction book from the shelf.

Write down the:

    Author: _____

    Title: _____

    Spine Label:

    Subject: _____

Does it have: (a) an index?   Yes/No

              (b) a contents page?   Yes/No

How do you use the index?

_____

_____

_____

Parts of a Non-fiction Book

Draw lines to join the words to the features found on the cover of the book.

TITLE

SPINE LABEL
(CALL
NUMBER)

AUTHOR

Choose a non-fiction book from the shelf. Write down the:

Author: _____

Title: _____

Illustrator: _____

Spine Label: _____

Publisher: _____

Index: (Yes/No)

Contents Page: (Yes/No)

Would you find using a book without an index easier or harder than one with an index? Why?

_____

_____

_____

_____

_____

Dewey Decimal System

Who invented the Dewey Decimal System? _____

What subjects are dealt with in the divisions? List two subdivisions under each of the divisions.

Division	**Subdivision**
000s _Generalities_	(1) _010 - Bibliography_
	(2) _070 - Journalism, Publishing, Newpapers_
100s _____	(1) _____
	(2) _____
200s _____	(1) _____
	(2) _____
300s _____	(1) _____
	(2) _____
400s _____	(1) _____
	(2) _____
500s _____	(1) _____
	(2) _____
600s _____	(1) _____
	(2) _____
700s _____	(1) _____
	(2) _____
800s _____	(1) _____
	(2) _____
900s _____	(1) _____
	(2) _____

Decimals

First look at the decimal numbers in front of the decimal point on these labels.

750.5	651.103	651.405	651.3	300.4
750.15	301.4	651.4	651.33	750.201

Put the decimal numbers in order as they would appear on the bookshelves.

1. _____   2. _____   3. _____

4. _____   5. _____   6. _____

7. _____   8. _____   9. _____

10. _____

Locate the books in your library with the same decimal numbers given above and complete the contents of the spine label.

300.4	301.4	_____	_____
_____	_____	_____	_____

   _____   _____

Using a
Subject Heading Index
(Non-automated Libraries)

The Subject Heading Index gives the Dewey decimal number of the subject.

What are the Dewey decimal numbers for the following subjects?

Computers ___e.g. 004___   Poetry_____

Animals _____   Trees _____

Cookery _____   Woodwork _____

Tennis _____   Tables _____

Mathematics _____   Fashion - clothing _____

Put the above into the order you would find them on the shelf.

Choose one of the above subjects on the shelf.

What subjects are found on either side of the book you have located?

_____   _____

Do these have anything in common with the book you chose?

_____

_____

_____

Write three interesting facts from the book you chose.

Title: _____

1. _____

2. _____

3. _____

Using a
Subject Heading Index
(Automated Libraries)

Which number is a Subject Search? _____

Give the Dewey decimal numbers for the following subjects:

Computers __e.g. 004_____   Poetry_____

Animals _____   Trees _____

Cookery _____   Woodwork _____

Tennis _____   Tables _____

Mathematics _____   Fashion - clothing _____

Put the above into the order you would find them on the shelf.

Choose one of the above subjects on the shelf.

What subjects are found on either side of the book you have located?

_____   _____

Do these have anything in common with the book you chose?

_____

_____

_____

Write three interesting facts from the book you chose.

Title: _____

1. _____

2. _____

3. _____

Using the Catalogue
(Non-automated Libraries)

Under what three headings will you need to be able to find a book?

* A _____

  * T _____

  * S _____

Try finding the books below. Remember, you are doing three different searches.

Author	Title	Subject
Ward, B	State Parliament	Dogs
Barrett, N	Space Shuttles	Football
Dugan, M	Money	Computers

Choose one of the above or locate your own book to record information below from each search.

AUTHOR: _____

Title: _____

Illustrator: _____

Publisher: _____

TITLE: _____

Author: _____

Illustrator: _____

Publisher: _____

SUBJECT: _____

Title: _____

Author: _____

Illustrator: _____

Publisher: _____

Using the Computers (Automated Libraries)

Draw the computer screen from the terminals. Include the instructions and help symbols.

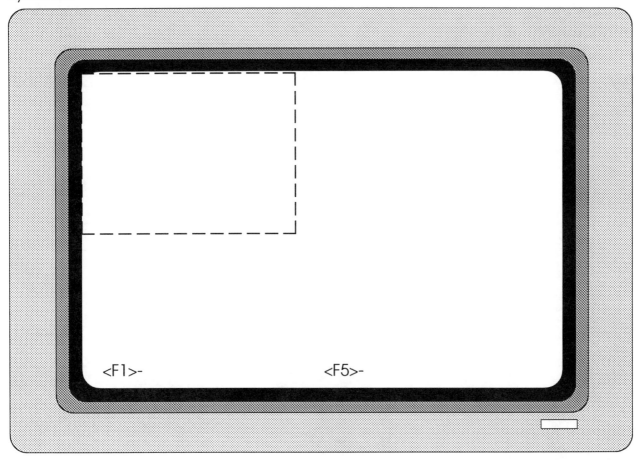

<F1>-   <F5>-

Under what three headings will you need to be able to find a book?

* A _____

* T _____

* S _____

Try finding the books below. Remember, you are doing three different searches.

Author	Title	Subject
Ward, B	State Parliament	Dogs
Barrett, N	Space Shuttles	Football
Dugan, M	Money	Computers

Choose a book from the shelves and complete the following:

SUBJECT: _____

Title: _____

Author: _____

Illustrator: _____

Publisher: _____

Index

Choose a non-fiction book. Check that it has an index.

How do you use a non-fiction index? _____

_____

Why is an index useful? _____

_____

_____

Look at the index of the book you have. Write down the subjects found on the following pages:

5. _____

7. _____

12. _____

1. _____

3. _____

Locate any page in your book.

Page number: _____

Subject: _____

From this page, write a brief summary. Include a diagram.

_____

_____

_____

_____

_____

_____

_____

_____

_____

_____

_____

_____

Dating a Book

Most books will tell you how old they are by the date they were published.

Copyright Date

Author

Title

> First published in 1906 Penguin Books Ltd
> Middlesex, United Kingdom
>
> Copyright 1906 Frederick Warne & Co.
>
> Potter, Beatrix
> The Story of A Fierce Bad Rabbit
>
> ISBN 0 7232 0611 2
>
> ○

Date of Publication

ISBN Number

All the above details are usually found at the front or the very back of a book.

Choose a book from the non-fiction shelf.

Locate the publishing details. Who was the publisher? _____

What is the date of publication? _____

What is the copyright date? _____

Find three more books and write the information down.

1.   Title: _____

    Publisher: _____

    Date of publication: _____

    Copyright date: _____

2.   Title: _____

    Publisher: _____

    Date of publication: _____

    Copyright date: _____

3.   Title: _____

    Publisher: _____

    Date of publication: _____

    Copyright date: _____

What is the Title of the book that is the:

    oldest? _____

    youngest? _____

Contents Page

Choose a non-fiction book. Check that it has a contents page.

How do you use a contents page? _____

_____

Why is a contents page useful? _____

_____

Look at the contents page of your book. Write down the titles of the following chapters.

1. _____

2. _____

3. _____

4. _____

5. _____

Locate the second chapter in your book. What is the chapter's heading?

_____

Write a brief summary explaining the chapter.

_____

_____

_____

_____

_____

_____

_____

_____

_____

_____

_____

_____

_____

_____

Plays

Plays are an example of a non-fiction subject.

Your teacher will give your class a play to read out together.

Title of the play: _____

In your group, select a play from the school library. You will be asked to perform this play in the next lesson.

Name of the play _____

Practise your play - work out who will play the different characters.

Character	Name
_____	_____
_____	_____
_____	_____
_____	_____
_____	_____
_____	_____
_____	_____
_____	_____

Write a description of your character and the role he/she plays.

_____

_____

_____

_____

_____

_____

_____

_____

_____

_____

 # Poetry

Poetry is another example of a non-fiction subject.

What is poetry? _____

_____

_____

_____

Listen to several poems read by your teacher.

Locate the poetry section on the shelves and find a poem you like. What are some characteristics you like about the poem you have chosen?

_____

_____

_____

_____

Write your own poem below.

Autobiographies vs Biographies

Explain the difference between an autobiography and a biography.

_____

_____

_____

_____

Write your own autobiography.

Consider the following information to include in your autobiography:

date of birth	place of birth	family and friends
interests/hobbies	achievements	ambitions

_____

_____

_____

_____

_____

_____

_____

_____

_____

_____

_____

_____

_____

_____

_____

_____

_____

_____

_____

_____

Biographies

Choose one of the following famous people and write his/her biography.

Marie Curie

Helen Adams Keller

Muhammad Ali

Michaelangelo Buonarroti

Florence Nightingale

Nadia Comaneci

Christopher Columbus

William Shakespeare

Theodore Roosevelt

Robert Louis Stevenson

Johann Bach

Guglielmo Marconi

Galileo Galilei

James Watt

You may like to write about someone of your own choice.

SUBJECT: _____

Write your notes below.

Personal details	Why famous	Achievements and important events	Effect he/she has on our life today
For example: Date of Birth Place of Birth Education	*For example : Inventor*		

Each of the above columns forms a paragraph. On a separate piece of paper provided, write a summary of your notes into four paragraphs.

Non-fiction Quiz

Explain what a non-fiction book is. _____
_____
_____

What are three examples of the subjects found on the non-fiction shelves?

1. _____

2. _____

3. _____

What Dewey number are these found at on the shelves?

1. _____

2. _____

3. _____

Choose one of the above subjects and locate a book on the shelves. Write down the following:

Author: _____

Title: _____

Date of Publication: _____

Spine Label: _____

Index: _____

Contents: _____

Publishing Details: _____

Complete the cover of this book with the above mentioned details. Include drawings if applicable.

Non-fiction Sleuth

N	O	N	F	I	C	C	A	L	L	N	U	M	B	E	R	T	I	O	N
B	D	E	W	E	Y	D	E	C	I	M	A	L	S	Y	S	T	E	M	S
T	W	O	Y	R	T	E	O	P	K	S	I	N	O	C	R	A	M	S	D
I	K	O	F	I	C	O	N	T	E	N	T	S	P	A	G	E	A	H	E
T	E	I	T	O	R	R	A	N	O	U	B	S	T	I	N	L	G	A	C
L	S	N	F	O	R	M	A	I	B	I	O	G	R	A	P	H	Y	K	I
E	P	O	N	B	S	P	I	N	E	L	A	B	E	L	Y	U	S	E	M
X	E	D	N	I	G	N	I	D	A	E	H	T	C	E	J	B	U	S	A
S	A	U	T	H	O	R	L	E	P	U	B	L	I	S	H	E	R	P	L
Y	R	I	N	D	E	X	A	N	O	I	T	C	I	F	N	O	N	E	S
A	Y	H	P	A	R	G	O	I	B	O	T	U	A	U	C	A	N	A	I
L	I	W	E	B	C	R	O	O	S	T	L	E	V	E	S	O	O	R	P
P	E	M	K	Q	B	Y	W	M	E	H	N	E	W	S	P	A	P	E	R

Locate these words.

Ali
Author
Autobiography
Biography
Buonarroti
Call Number
Contents Page
Decimals
Dewey Decimal System
Index
Marconi

Newspaper
Non-fiction
Poetry
Plays
Publisher
Roosevelt
Shakespeare
Spine Label
Subject Heading Index
Title
Watt

Reference Books

What are reference books? _____
_____
_____
_____

Write what you know about each of these reference books.

Encyclopaedia: _____
_____
_____

Thesaurus: _____
_____
_____

Atlas: _____
_____
_____

Telephone Book: _____
_____
_____

Street Directory: _____
_____
_____

Year Book: _____
_____
_____

Dictionary: _____
_____
_____

DICTIONARY   STREET DIRECTORY   YEAR BOOK   TELEPHONE BOOK

Using Encyclopaedias 1

Look at the encyclopaedia index. Locate the following subjects. Write down the volume and/or page number of the subject.

	Volume	Page No.
Animals	_____	_____
England	_____	_____
Chemistry	_____	_____
Australia	_____	_____
Wind	_____	_____
Bradman, Donald	_____	_____
Flowers	_____	_____
Trees	_____	_____
Greece	_____	_____
Vatican City	_____	_____

Choose one of the subjects. Locate it in the encyclopaedia.

Write a brief summary of your topic.

_____

_____

_____

_____

_____

_____

_____

_____

_____

_____

_____

Draw a picture on the topic.

Using Encyclopaedias 2

Choose a topic of interest to you. _____

Locate it in the encyclopaedias.

Encyclopaedia Name: _____

Volume: _____ Page Number: _____

Write a brief summary of your topic. Include a diagram.

_____

_____

_____

_____

_____

_____

_____

_____

_____

_____

_____

_____

_____

_____

_____

_____

_____

_____

_____

_____

_____

_____

_____

_____

Using Dictionaries

Describe what a dictionary is used for and how it is used.

_____

_____

_____

_____

Provide the meaning of the following words.

ooze: _____

_____

pole: _____

_____

epigram: _____

_____

scribe:_____

_____

hasty: _____

_____

theory: _____

_____

welfare: _____

_____

aorta: _____

_____

book: _____

_____

condition:_____

_____

Using the Telephone Book 1

Telephone books contain the addresses and phone numbers of private homes and business. They also contain information such as postcodes and emergency numbers.

___ ___ ___ ___ ___ ___ ___ ___ ___ ___ ___ ___ ___ ___ ___ are alphabetically listed. Put the following into alphabetical order.

Green S. L. & P. R.   1. _____

Green Photography   2. _____

Green A.K.   3. _____

Green as Grass Nursery   4. _____

Green S. T.   5. _____

Sample telephone directory

```
Bell GardenCentre,
        Bellair Crs, Red St CV23 7PY ........ Stratford-on-A    3469 482
Bell Graphics Ltd, 7 Pink St BSU 2BG ............... Bidford-on-A    7178 903
Bell G & R, 23 Pond St CV5 4GW.......................... Coventry    7181 231
Bell G T, 54 Stanley St CV38 0LD ............................. Kineton    6123 777
Bell H, 1 Brighton St CV34 4JN ............................... Keresley    4567 256
Bell H, 9 Orange St CV22 4CR ...................................... Rugby    1234 490
Bell H.E.J., 29 Stewart St CV32 4IP ............ Leamington Spa    9876 877
Bell H & P, 11 Station Av CV17 02W ............. Stratford-on-A    4567 383
Bell Inn, 34 Banham Rd CV6 3FN .......................... Keresley    8765 289
Bell I.S., 1 St. Georges St CV2 1NB ....................... Coventry    5678 292
Bell I.J.L. 345 Aberfoyle Cres CV7 3HP ................. Coventry    7654 856
Bell J, River St CV8 3PR ............................................. Keresley    6789 490
Bell J.A., Rose Cott.,  Willow Cres CV6 9JW ......... Coventry    6543 000
```

Write down the address and phone number of the following names:

Bell Graphics _____

Bell H.E.J. _____

Bell J.A. _____

Bell Garden Centre _____

Bell I.S. _____

Write down the names of six local towns in your area and their postal codes.

_____   _____

_____   _____

_____   _____

Using the Telephone Book 2

Using the index to the Yellow Pages, write down the page(s) on which you would find the following subjects.

Acupuncture _____

Boxes and cases - wood _____

Child care centres _____

Dance wear _____

Information services _____

Power steering _____

Panel beaters _____

School supplies _____

Quarries _____

Tool makers _____

Locate one of the subjects.

How many places are mentioned under this heading? _____

Is there one near you? _____

If not, which is the closest? _____

Explain the uses that the following people would have for the Yellow Pages.

1. A musician _____

_____

_____

2. A student _____

_____

_____

3. What number would you call for the following information?

(a) Alcohol and Drug Information Service _____

(b) Aids/HIV Helpline _____

(c) Wake-up and Reminder calls _____

(d) RSPCA _____

(e) Faults and Service Difficulties _____

Notemaking

Read the passage below. Underline all the key words and phrases.

INSECTS

Insects come in many shapes and forms, from butterflies to ants and from grasshoppers to flies. However, all insects have the following features in common. A fully grown adult can be divided into three parts: the head, the thorax and the abdomen.

The mouthparts, eyes and antennae are all found on the insect's head. Most insects have more than two eyes - some have two large eyes and three smaller ones.

The thorax is the middle part of an insect's body. The wings and legs are attached to the thorax. All adult insects have six legs. (Spiders have eight legs; therefore, they are not insects.) One or two pairs of wings are also attached to the thorax.

The end part of an insect is called the abdomen. If an insect has an additional pair of feelers they are usually found at the end of their abdomen.

Insects eat and breathe very differently from us. Insects don't breathe through their mouths, but through small holes in the side of their thorax and abdomen. These are called spiracles. They also have many different ways of feeding; for example, grasshoppers and beetles have mouths that can bite and chew, whereas a bee has mouthparts (proboscis) that allow it to suck and chew.

Although insects come in such a variety of shapes and forms, they all have certain things in common. Every insect, at some point, has six legs, a pair of wings and a pair of compound eyes.

Their bodies can be divided into three parts - the head, thorax and abdomen. In all, insects have been in the world for millions of years, and are still likely to be found wherever you go.

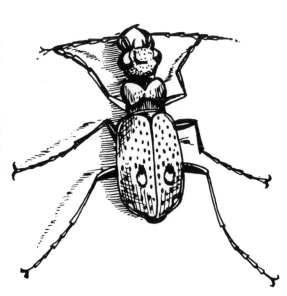

Notemaking (Continued)

Using this and any other information you have, fill in the explosion chart.

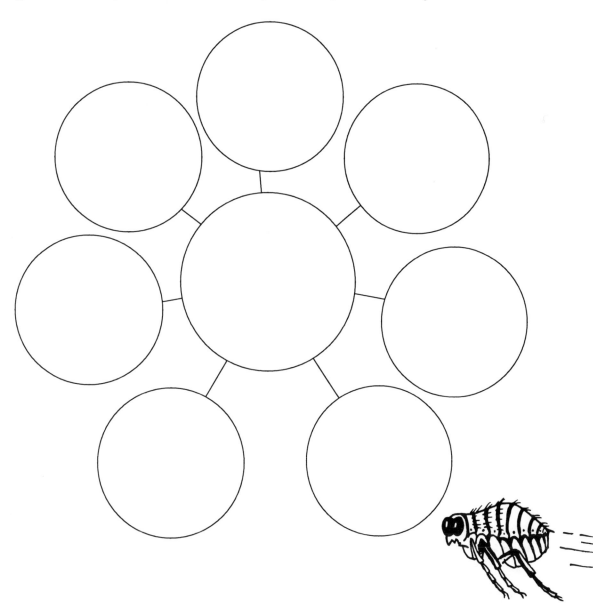

Write a sentence briefly describing each heading on the explosion chart.

A. _____

B. _____

C. _____

D. _____

E. _____

F. _____

G. _____

Notemaking (Continued)

Put these sentences in order and write a few paragraphs of information.

_____

_____

_____

_____

_____

_____

_____

_____

_____

_____

_____

_____

_____

_____

_____

_____

_____

_____

_____

_____

_____

_____

Review this information and write a final draft.

Reference Quiz

Write down four examples of reference books. Briefly explain the purpose of, and how to use, each of them.

Choose one of the above reference books. Explain in detail the type of information it presents and the correct way to use it.

Explain how an index is used.

Wordsleuth

S	A	X	C	O	N	T	E	N	T	S	P	A	G	E	B	V	X	W	A
U	A	E	S	P	I	N	E	L	A	B	E	L	X	D	C	V	D	E	U
R	U	D	E	W	E	Y	D	E	C	I	M	A	L	C	K	E	E	X	D
J	B	N	C	O	F	I	C	T	I	O	N	B	G	L	F	R	K	F	I
U	E	I	P	Q	P	N	E	T	W	M	O	D	H	Z	G	T	Y	L	O
C	R	S	R	E	P	A	P	S	W	E	N	I	J	O	Q	I	M	L	V
T	S	C	S	Q	O	G	F	A	R	E	F	E	R	E	N	C	E	I	I
H	G	A	T	R	X	T	V	N	P	J	I	H	R	I	N	A	N	T	S
E	N	L	V	I	D	E	O	Y	U	C	C	S	C	P	T	L	C	E	U
A	I	L	J	I	I	L	L	R	B	A	T	L	A	S	P	F	Y	R	A
D	K	N	K	H	S	E	U	A	L	T	I	C	R	D	O	I	C	A	L
I	A	U	L	Z	P	V	M	N	I	A	O	T	E	H	S	L	L	T	F
N	M	M	M	I	L	I	E	O	S	L	N	I	E	E	T	E	O	U	G
G	E	B	J	U	A	S	Z	I	H	O	B	T	R	Z	E	U	P	R	T
B	T	E	V	G	Y	I	F	T	E	G	A	L	S	X	R	V	E	E	R
O	O	R	H	Y	S	O	Y	C	R	U	Z	E	R	C	S	W	D	D	O
O	N	X	W	K	A	N	B	I	S	E	A	U	T	H	O	R	I	E	P
K	E	Y	W	O	R	D	S	D	T	S	E	N	I	Z	A	G	A	M	S

Locate these words.

Atlas	Dictionary	Notemaking	Subject Heading Book
Audiovisual	Displays	Newspapers	Television
Author	Encyclopaedia	Non-fiction	Title
Call number	Fiction	Posters	Vertical File
Careers	Index	Publisher	Video
Catalogue	Key words	Reference	Volume
Contents Page	Literature	Spine label	Atlas
Dewey Decimal	Magazines	Sport	

Periodicals

Periodicals are materials that contain up-to-date information.

Examples are magazines and pamphlets. Newspapers which appear less often than daily are also called periodicals. Daily newspapers are not classed as periodicals as they do not appear periodically.

<u>Why are periodicals useful</u>?

The information they present is more up-to-date than any book could possibly be.

Look through pamphlets, magazines and newspapers. Find some interesting and informative articles relating to a topic you are studying in class. Put these in your booklets or files behind this sheet.

Glue your most interesting article below.

Vertical File

The vertical file contains up-to-date information on current topics which can not easily be found in non-fiction books.

1. What is the vertical file? _____

_____

2. How is the vertical file arranged?

   Put the following into the order you would find them in the vertical file.

   ☐ Road Safety   ☐ Animals - cruelty to

   ☐ Aids   ☐ Natural Disasters

   ☐ Nutrition   ☐ Drugs

3. What type of information can be found in the vertical file? _____

_____

4. Why is the vertical file so useful? _____

_____

5. Is there another area in the library where magazines are kept? If so, where?
   Mark it in the plan. _____

_____

_____

6. Select a file from the vertical file.

   Subject: _____

   What information was contained in the file?

   Newspaper Articles: _____

   _____

   _____

   Pamphlets: _____

   _____

   _____

   Other: _____

   _____

   _____

Periodicals Quiz

1. What are periodicals? _____

2. Give three examples.

    (a) _____

    (b) _____

    (c) _____

3. Why is a daily newspaper not classed as a periodical?

    _____

    _____

4. Is a Sunday newspaper classed as a periodical? Why?

    _____

    _____

4. What type of information can you find in periodicals?

    _____

    _____

5. What is a vertical file?

    _____

    _____

6. How is a vertical file arranged?

    _____

    _____

7. What kinds of subjects are found in the vertical file? Give three examples.

    _____

    _____

    _____

8. Where is the vertical file located?

    _____

    _____

    _____

    _____

Research 1

Selecting from all the resources in the library, present a report on an animal of your choice.

Subject: _____

Travel	
Habitat	
Food	
Body	

Complete your notes in the chart above.

Once finished, write your notes into four paragraphs on a separate sheet of paper. Include a list of the books used to obtain the information for your table and draw/paste a picture of your animal.

Research 2

Selecting from all the resources in the library, choose a sport to research. Write your notes below. You may wish to change one of the subheadings.

Famous Players	
Equipment	
Rules	
History	

Write your notes into paragraphs on a piece of blank paper. Include a picture of your choice relating to the sport you have chosen. For example: equipment, famous player.

Bingo

Requirements
One card per student
Counters
Word cards (for bingo caller)

What to do:
Students are given a card. The Bingo caller chooses a word and calls it out clearly. The first person to cover all the words on his or her card with the counters calls 'Bingo' and is the winner.

Atlas	Index	Author
Library	Catalogue	Non-fiction
Dewey Decimal	Contents Page	Computers
Reference	Dictionary	Spine Label
Fiction	Title	Encyclopaedia

Bingo

library	non-fiction	reference
computers	author	Dewey decimal
contents page	catalogue	title

library	fiction	non-fiction
reference	computers	atlas
catalogue	author	dictionary

Dewey decimal	contents page	index
fiction	non-fiction	computers
dictionary	reference	author

library	author	Dewey decimal
computers	fiction	non-fiction
spine label	title	index

author	computers	catalogue
index	reference	fiction
non-fiction	title	library

encyclopaedia	index	library
spine label	author	computers
fiction	non-fiction	reference

computers	author	atlas
Dewey decimal	title	encyclopaedia
index	fiction	non-fiction

index	catalogue	Dewey decimal
encyclopaedia	spine label	library
title	atlas	fiction

non-fiction	reference	spine label
atlas	index	title
dictionary	contents page	Dewey decimal

library	spine label	fiction
non-fiction	reference	index
catalogue	atlas	title

Further Research 1

1. What kind of adaptations do animals have to help them survive?

   _____

   _____

   _____

2. How can matter be changed from one state to another?

   solid-liquid-gas _____

   _____

3. Fungi and ferns are both plants. Do they live in similar environments?

   Explain how they live. _____

   _____

   _____

4. Which substances can conduct electricity? _____

   _____

5. What is weather? Why is it constantly changing? _____

   _____

   _____

6. How does the climate, rainfall and soil type determine the type of farming in a particular area?

   _____

   _____

   _____

7. What kind of livestock are found on farms and how do they differ from country to country?

   _____

   _____

   _____

8. Why do birds and animals migrate? _____

   _____

9. What equipment did farmers use in earlier times? _____

   _____

   _____

Further Research 2

10. What is the difference between a millimetre, a centimetre and a metre?

    _____

    _____

11. What was 'D Day'? Why was it important? _____

    _____

    _____

12. Who painted the Mona Lisa? Name two other famous pieces of work this
    artist created. _____

    _____

13. What is the braille system? Who invented it? _____

    _____

14. Name the layers of the earth. _____

    _____

    _____

15. Name and describe three water forms. _____

    (a) _____

    _____

    (b) _____

    _____

    (c) _____

16. Name three members of the British Commonwealth._____

    _____

    _____

17. What are the elements that make water?_____

    _____

18. What sort of animal is a *feline*? Name three members of that family.

    _____

    _____

    _____

    _____